Health for Life
Test Book

Authors

Julius B. Richmond
John D. MacArthur Professor of
    Health Policy
Director, Division of Health Policy
    Research and Education
Harvard University
Adviser on Child Health Policy
Children's Hospital of Boston
Boston, Massachusetts

Elenore T. Pounds
Health Education Writer
Downers Grove, Illinois

Physical Fitness Author

Charles B. Corbin
Professor, Department of Health
    and Physical Education
Arizona State University
Tempe, Arizona

Scott, Foresman and Company
Editorial Offices: Glenview, Illinois

Regional Offices: Sunnyvale, California ●
Tucker, Georgia ● Glenview, Illinois ●
Oakland, New Jersey ● Dallas, Texas

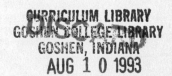

Reviewers and Contributors

Lourdes Alcorta-Rogover
Educational Consultant
Former Teacher
Miami, Florida

Matthew Bustamante
Bilingual/Cross-Cultural
Education Specialist
Bandini Elementary School
Montebello, California

Rosalyn Gantt
Teacher
Midway Elementary School
Cincinnati, Ohio

Jon Hisgen
School Health Coordinator
Pewaukee Public Schools
Pewaukee, Wisconsin

Jeanne Mannings
Teacher
Adamsville Elementary School
Atlanta, Georgia

Candace Purdy
Health Teacher
Maine South High School
Park Ridge, Illinois

Shirley Van Sickle
Health Teacher
DeVeaux Junior High School
Toledo, Ohio

ISBN: 0-673-29674-1

Contents

To the Teacher

This test book contains two two-page tests for each of the chapters in the Scott, Foresman *Health for Life* series.

The two tests for each chapter contain different questions, but TEST A and TEST B are equivalent in content covered and difficulty. This format provides an extra test that can be used as a pre-test, post-test, or make-up test. Each chapter test is divided into three parts. On the first page are the multiple choice questions. The questions on the second page of the test require the student to match terms with their definitions, fill in the blanks in sentences, or answer questions that require students to synthesize, apply, and draw conclusions from the material studied.

A Student Progress Chart is supplied on page 7. Students can use a copy of this chart to keep a record of their test scores and to chart their progress. Also, on page 6 is a Percentage Conversion Chart for your convenience.

Use of the Blackline Masters
The blackline masters in this book may be reproduced for classroom use by photocopying, offset printing, or spirit duplicating. They may be reproduced for classroom use by schools that use Scott, Foresman *Health for Life* without the prior written permission of Scott, Foresman and Company.

Percentage Conversion Table

This table will help you quickly convert a raw test score to a percentage score for any test containing up to 40 items.

Directions for using the table

Example: There are 28 items on a test, and a student correctly answers 22 of them.

1. Find the number of items, 28, along the left side of the table.

2. Place a ruler or a strip of paper under the row for 28.

3. Find the column for 22, the number of items correctly answered.

4. Go down the column for 22 until you come to the row for 28. The number 79 is the percentage score.

Number of Items →

Number Correct →

Items	1	2	3	4	5	6	7	8	9	10	11	12	13	14	15	16	17	18	19	20	21	22	23	24	25	26	27	28	29	30	31	32	33	34	35	36	37	38	39	40
1	100																																							
2	50	100																																						
3	33	67	100																																					
4	25	50	75	100																																				
5	20	40	60	80	100																																			
6	17	33	50	67	83	100																																		
7	14	29	43	57	71	86	100																																	
8	13	25	38	50	63	75	88	100																																
9	11	22	33	44	56	67	78	89	100																															
10	10	20	30	40	50	60	70	80	90	100																														
11	9	18	27	36	45	55	64	73	82	91	100																													
12	8	17	25	33	42	50	58	67	75	83	92	100																												
13	8	15	23	31	38	46	54	62	69	77	85	92	100																											
14	7	14	21	29	36	43	50	57	64	71	79	86	93	100																										
15	7	13	20	27	33	40	47	53	60	67	73	80	87	93	100																									
16	6	13	19	25	31	38	44	50	56	63	69	75	81	88	94	100																								
17	6	12	18	24	29	35	41	47	53	59	65	71	76	82	88	94	100																							
18	6	11	17	22	28	33	39	44	50	56	61	67	72	78	83	89	94	100																						
19	5	11	16	21	26	32	37	42	47	53	58	63	68	74	79	84	89	95	100																					
20	5	10	15	20	25	30	35	40	45	50	55	60	65	70	75	80	85	90	95	100																				
21	5	10	14	19	24	29	33	38	43	48	52	57	62	67	71	76	81	86	90	95	100																			
22	5	9	14	18	23	27	32	36	41	45	50	55	59	64	68	73	77	82	86	91	95	100																		
23	4	9	13	17	22	26	30	35	39	43	48	52	57	61	65	70	74	78	83	87	91	96	100																	
24	4	8	13	17	21	25	29	33	38	42	46	50	54	58	63	67	71	75	79	83	88	92	96	100																
25	4	8	12	16	20	24	28	32	36	40	44	48	52	56	60	64	68	72	76	80	84	88	92	96	100															
26	4	8	12	15	19	23	27	31	35	38	42	46	50	54	58	62	65	69	73	77	81	85	88	92	96	100														
27	4	7	11	15	19	22	26	30	33	37	41	44	48	52	56	59	63	67	70	74	78	81	85	89	93	96	100													
28	4	7	11	14	18	21	25	29	32	36	39	43	46	50	54	57	61	64	68	71	75	79	82	86	89	93	96	100												
29	3	7	10	14	17	21	24	28	31	34	38	41	45	48	52	55	59	62	66	69	72	76	79	83	86	90	93	97	100											
30	3	7	10	13	17	20	23	27	30	33	37	40	43	47	50	53	57	60	63	67	70	73	77	80	83	87	90	93	97	100										
31	3	6	10	13	16	19	23	26	29	32	35	39	42	45	48	52	55	58	61	65	68	71	74	77	81	84	87	90	94	97	100									
32	3	6	9	13	16	19	22	25	28	31	34	38	41	44	47	50	53	56	59	63	66	69	72	75	78	81	84	88	91	94	97	100								
33	3	6	9	12	15	18	21	24	27	30	33	36	39	42	45	48	52	55	58	61	64	67	70	73	76	79	82	85	88	91	94	97	100							
34	3	6	9	12	15	18	21	24	26	29	32	35	38	41	44	47	50	53	56	59	62	65	68	71	74	76	79	82	85	88	91	94	97	100						
35	3	6	9	11	14	17	20	23	26	29	31	34	37	40	43	46	49	51	54	57	60	63	66	69	71	74	77	80	83	86	89	91	94	97	100					
36	3	6	8	11	14	17	19	22	25	28	31	33	36	39	42	44	47	50	53	56	58	61	64	67	69	72	75	78	81	83	86	89	92	94	97	100				
37	3	5	8	11	14	16	19	22	24	27	30	32	35	38	41	43	46	49	51	54	57	59	62	65	68	70	73	76	78	81	84	86	89	92	95	97	100			
38	3	5	8	11	13	16	18	21	24	26	29	32	34	37	39	42	45	47	50	53	55	58	61	63	66	68	71	74	76	79	82	84	87	89	92	95	97	100		
39	3	5	8	10	13	15	18	21	23	26	28	31	33	36	38	41	44	46	49	51	54	56	59	62	64	67	69	72	74	77	79	82	85	87	90	92	95	97	100	
40	3	5	8	10	13	15	18	20	23	25	28	30	33	35	38	40	43	45	48	50	53	55	58	60	63	65	68	70	73	75	78	80	83	85	88	90	93	95	98	100

Name _____

Student Progress Chart

Directions: This Student Progress Chart should be used to keep a record of your test scores. Each time you receive a chapter test score, fill in the chart to indicate your score. By doing this for every test you take, you will have a complete record of your progress. (Use the sample Student Progress Chart to the right as an example.)

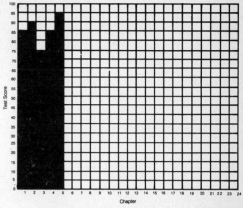

Sample Student Progress Chart

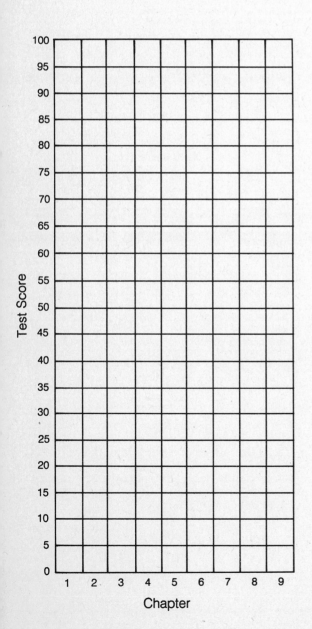

Name _____

Multiple Choice   Choose the best answer.

1. Since all people are different, each person is
   a. friendly.
   b. special.
   c. happy.
   d. strange.

2. A person who feels good about himself or herself
   a. has a good self-image.
   b. will always have many friends.
   c. is different from others.
   d. has no weaknesses.

3. What can cause people to feel upset?
   a. watching a movie
   b. a good self-image
   c. laughing with friends
   d. worry or anger

4. How might a person feel if he or she is treated unfairly?
   a. guilty
   b. happy
   c. foolish
   d. angry

5. What is the one good way to deal with anger?
   a. talk things over
   b. pretend nothing happened
   c. watch television
   d. punch a pillow

6. People who like each other
   a. never have disagreements.
   b. disagree all the time.
   c. have the same ideas.
   d. can have disagreements.

7. People can work out problems when they learn how to
   a. settle disagreements.
   b. use sign language.
   c. argue well.
   d. obey the rules.

8. In a disagreement, each person should be willing to
   a. listen to the other person.
   b. be silent about his or her ideas.
   c. argue as much as possible.
   d. accept the other one's ideas.

9. What is the best reason for using the decision-making steps?
   a. to make friends
   b. to make wise choices
   c. to improve spelling
   d. to win arguments

10. When making a decision, a person could make a list of
    a. things to do.
    b. his or her friends.
    c. possible choices.
    d. all personal problems.

Short Answer   Match each meaning in Column I with the correct word or words in Column II. Write the correct letter on the blank.

Column I	**Column II**
____ 11. something a person does well	a. appreciate
	b. self-image
____ 12. what a person thinks of himself or herself	c. disagreement
____ 13. to think highly of someone	d. strength
____ 14. a difference in what people think	

Short Essay   Write your answers in complete sentences.

15. Joshua has a good self-image, but he does not do well in sports. His friends have asked him to join their soccer team. What might he do?

_____

_____

_____.

16. Karla does not feel well. Her piano lesson is today, and she wishes she had spent more time practicing. What might be causing her to feel bad?

_____

_____

_____

Name _____

Multiple Choice Choose the best answer.

1. If a person is a good runner, then running is one of his or her
   a. weaknesses.
   b. games.
   c. goals.
   d. strengths.

2. People can make more friends and learn new things if they
   a. avoid people who are different.
   b. ignore their strengths.
   c. appreciate differences in people.
   d. keep their ideas to themselves.

3. Feelings
   a. are a sign of illness.
   b. can affect the way the body works.
   c. are felt by only a few people.
   d. are best ignored.

4. Anger and worry
   a. affect people in different ways.
   b. cause everyone to sweat.
   c. are wrong to feel.
   d. make the heart beat slower.

5. One helpful way to deal with angry feelings is to
   a. argue with someone.
   b. hide.
   c. ignore them.
   d. talk things over.

6. What happens to angry feelings that a person keeps inside?
   a. They go away.
   b. They show up sooner or later.
   c. They become good feelings after a few months.
   d. They slow down the heart rate.

7. People who want to settle disagreements with others could
   a. refuse to see each other.
   b. talk things over.
   c. keep their ideas to themselves.
   d. yell at each other.

8. When people cannot settle a disagreement, they need to
   a. argue about it.
   b. be unpleasant.
   c. flip a coin.
   d. agree to disagree.

9. To make a wise decision, a person must
   a. do what other people want.
   b. argue with others.
   c. grow up.
   d. realize a decision is needed.

10. Using the decision-making steps can help a person
    a. make good choices.
    b. do better in school.
    c. become stronger.
    d. appreciate others.

Short Answer Put the five decision-making steps in order by numbering them 1 through 5. Write the answer on the blanks.

____ 11. Decide which choice is best.

____ 12. List the possible choices.

____ 13. Realize that a decision is needed.

____ 14. Judge the decision.

____ 15. List the possible results of each choice.

Short Essay Write your answers in complete sentences.

16. Maria's gym class is learning how to play soccer. Maria has never done well in sports and does not want to look foolish in front of her friends. What can Maria do?

_____

_____

_____

17. On the day of an important test, Diane had a headache, and Mike had a stomachache. If they were not sick, explain what could be happening.

_____

_____

18. Both Paul and Jan say that it is their turn to work at the computer. How can they settle their disagreement?

_____

_____

Multiple Choice   Choose the best answer.

1. Since all people are different, each person is
   a. friendly.
   b. special.
   c. happy.
   d. strange.

2. A person who feels good about himself or herself
   a. has a good self-image.
   b. will always have many friends.
   c. is different from others.
   d. has no weaknesses.

3. What can cause people to feel upset?
   a. watching a movie
   b. a good self-image
   c. laughing with friends
   d. worry or anger

4. How might a person feel if he or she is treated unfairly?
   a. guilty
   b. happy
   c. foolish
   d. angry

5. What is the one good way to deal with anger?
   a. talk things over
   b. pretend nothing happened
   c. watch television
   d. punch a pillow

6. People who like each other
   a. never have disagreements.
   b. disagree all the time.
   c. have the same ideas.
   d. can have disagreements.

7. People can work out problems when they learn how to
   a. settle disagreements.
   b. use sign language.
   c. argue well.
   d. obey the rules.

8. In a disagreement, each person should be willing to
   a. listen to the other person.
   b. be silent about his or her ideas.
   c. argue as much as possible.
   d. accept the other one's ideas.

9. What is the best reason for using the decision-making steps?
   a. to make friends
   b. to make wise choices
   c. to improve spelling
   d. to win arguments

10. When making a decision, a person could make a list of
    a. things to do.
    b. his or her friends.
    c. possible choices.
    d. all personal problems.

Name _____

Short Answer Match each meaning in Column I with the correct word or words in Column II. Write the correct letter on the blank.

Column I

d 11. something a person does well

b 12. what a person thinks of himself or herself

a 13. to think highly of someone

c 14. a difference in what people think

Column II

a. appreciate

b. self-image

c. disagreement

d. strength

Short Essay Write your answers in complete sentences.

15. Joshua has a good self-image, but he does not do well in sports. His friends have asked him to join their soccer team. What might he do?

   Answers might include: Joshua could try out for the

   team and try his best to improve; or he could say

   no to his friends and do something else he enjoys.

16. Karla does not feel well. Her piano lesson is today, and she wishes she had spent more time practicing. What might be causing her to feel bad?

   Karla might feel bad because she is worried about

   her piano lesson. Worrying about something can often

   make a person feel sick.

Multiple Choice   Choose the best answer.

1. If a person is a good runner, then running is one of his or her
   a. weaknesses.
   b. games.
   c. goals.
   d. strengths.

2. People can make more friends and learn new things if they
   a. avoid people who are different.
   b. ignore their strengths.
   c. appreciate differences in people.
   d. keep their ideas to themselves.

3. Feelings
   a. are a sign of illness.
   b. can affect the way the body works.
   c. are felt by only a few people.
   d. are best ignored.

4. Anger and worry
   a. affect people in different ways.
   b. cause everyone to sweat.
   c. are wrong to feel.
   d. make the heart beat slower.

5. One helpful way to deal with angry feelings is to
   a. argue with someone.
   b. hide.
   c. ignore them.
   d. talk things over.

6. What happens to angry feelings that a person keeps inside?
   a. They go away.
   b. They show up sooner or later.
   c. They become good feelings after a few months.
   d. They slow down the heart rate.

7. People who want to settle disagreements with others could
   a. refuse to see each other.
   b. talk things over.
   c. keep their ideas to themselves.
   d. yell at each other.

8. When people cannot settle a disagreement, they need to
   a. argue about it.
   b. be unpleasant.
   c. flip a coin.
   d. agree to disagree.

9. To make a wise decision, a person must
   a. do what other people want.
   b. argue with others.
   c. grow up.
   d. realize a decision is needed.

10. Using the decision-making steps can help a person
   a. make good choices.
   b. do better in school.
   c. become stronger.
   d. appreciate others.

Short Answer   Put the five decision-making steps in order by numbering them 1 through 5. Write the answer on the blanks.

__4__ 11. Decide which choice is best.

__2__ 12. List the possible choices.

__1__ 13. Realize that a decision is needed.

__5__ 14. Judge the decision.

__3__ 15. List the possible results of each choice.

Short Essay   Write your answers in complete sentences.

16. Maria's gym class is learning how to play soccer. Maria has never done well in sports and does not want to look foolish in front of her friends. What can Maria do?

   Maria can try hard and do the best she can. If

   she plays poorly, she should accept her weakness.

   Her friends will probably respect her for her effort.

17. On the day of an important test, Diane had a headache, and Mike had a stomachache. If they were not sick, explain what could be happening.

   They were nervous and worried. The feelings

   affected their bodies in different ways.

18. Both Paul and Jan say that it is their turn to work at the computer. How can they settle their disagreement?

   They can talk it over. If they cannot agree,

   they can agree to work out some type of solution.

Name _____

Multiple Choice   Choose the best answer.

1. The smallest living parts of your body are
   a. organs.
   b. cells.
   c. systems.
   d. bones.

2. Two or more kinds of body tissue grouped together form
   a. a cell.
   b. an organ.
   c. a system.
   d. a nerve.

3. A group of organs and body parts that works together is a
   a. cell.
   b. tissue.
   c. system.
   d. building block.

4. The heart is part of the
   a. circulatory system.
   b. nervous system.
   c. digestive system.
   d. respiratory system.

5. Blood passing through the lungs takes in a fresh supply of
   a. air.
   b. oxygen.
   c. cells.
   d. carbon dioxide.

6. Blood picks up nutrients from the
   a. heart.
   b. digestive system.
   c. esophagus.
   d. nervous system.

7. When you breathe out, you get rid of
   a. carbon dioxide.
   b. oxygen.
   c. bronchial tubes.
   d. air sacs.

8. The system that carries information to and from the brain is the
   a. circulatory system.
   b. respiratory system.
   c. digestive system.
   d. nervous system.

9. Nerves in the body are connected to the brain by the
   a. heart.
   b. spinal cord.
   c. blood vessels.
   d. backbone.

10. People grow
    a. until they are the same size.
    b. until they become 21 years old.
    c. at the same rate.
    d. at different rates.

Short Answer   Use the diagram to identify the parts.
Write the correct letter on each blank.

____ 11. Food tube

____ 12. Small intestine

____ 13. Stomach

____ 14. Large intestine

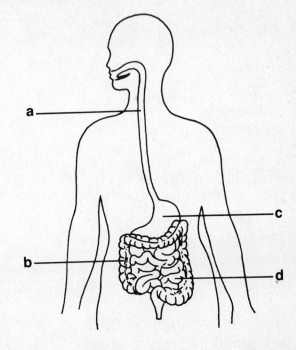

Short Essay   Write your answers in complete sentences.

15. Why does your body need to change food by
digesting it?

_____

_____

_____

16. What might happen if you injured your spinal cord?

_____

_____

_____

Multiple Choice   Choose the best answer.

1. The body's building blocks
   are
   a. cells.
   b. organs.
   c. tissues.
   d. systems.

2. An organ is made up of two or
   more kinds of
   a. systems.
   b. tissues.
   c. nerves.
   d. muscles.

3. Your pulse is caused by
   a. blood moving.
   b. air in your lungs.
   c. your arm muscles.
   d. digestive juices.

4. The heart and blood vessels are
   part of the
   a. circulatory system.
   b. digestive system.
   c. respiratory system.
   d. nervous system.

5. The blood gives off carbon
   dioxide and picks up oxygen in
   the
   a. muscles.
   b. arteries.
   c. heart.
   d. lungs.

6. The digestive system changes
   food so that the body gets
   needed
   a. carbon dioxide.
   b. tissues.
   c. nutrients.
   d. capillaries.

7. Lungs and air sacs are part of
   the
   a. digestive system.
   b. respiratory system.
   c. circulatory system.
   d. nervous system.

8. Motor nerves and sensory
   nerves are part of the
   a. nervous system.
   b. circulatory system.
   c. respiratory system.
   d. digestive system.

9. When you reach adult size, your
   bones
   a. stop growing.
   b. grow longer.
   c. grow heavier.
   d. become softer.

10. A body that works the way it
    should is always
    a. fast.
    b. big.
    c. strong.
    d. healthy.

Short Answer Use the diagram to answer the questions.
Write the correct letter in each blank.

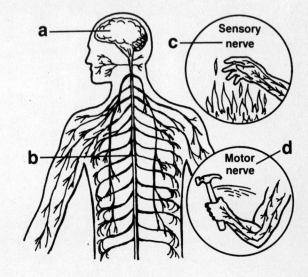

____ 11. This connects the nerves in your body to your brain.

____ 12. This kind of nerve carries messages to your brain.

____ 13. This kind of nerve carries messages from your brain.

____ 14. This organ gathers information from your senses.

Short Essay Write your answers in complete sentences.

15. How do your circulatory system and your respiratory system work together?

_____

_____

_____

_____

_____

16. What might happen if your brain did not help control your breathing all the time?

_____

_____

Name _____

Multiple Choice   Choose the best answer.

1. The smallest living parts of your body are
   a. organs.
   (b.) cells.
   c. systems.
   d. bones.

2. Two or more kinds of body tissue grouped together form
   a. a cell.
   (b.) an organ.
   c. a system.
   d. a nerve.

3. A group of organs and body parts that works together is a
   a. cell.
   b. tissue.
   (c.) system.
   d. building block.

4. The heart is part of the
   (a.) circulatory system.
   b. nervous system.
   c. digestive system.
   d. respiratory system.

5. Blood passing through the lungs takes in a fresh supply of
   a. air.
   (b.) oxygen.
   c. cells.
   d. carbon dioxide.

6. Blood picks up nutrients from the
   a. heart.
   (b.) digestive system.
   c. esophagus.
   d. nervous system.

7. When you breathe out, you get rid of
   (a.) carbon dioxide.
   b. oxygen.
   c. bronchial tubes.
   d. air sacs.

8. The system that carries information to and from the brain is the
   a. circulatory system.
   b. respiratory system.
   c. digestive system.
   (d.) nervous system.

9. Nerves in the body are connected to the brain by the
   a. heart.
   (b.) spinal cord.
   c. blood vessels.
   d. backbone.

10. People grow
   a. until they are the same size.
   b. until they become 21 years old.
   c. at the same rate.
   (d.) at different rates.

Short Answer   Use the diagram to identify the parts.
Write the correct letter on each blank.

_a_ 11. Food tube

_d_ 12. Small intestine

_c_ 13. Stomach

_b_ 14. Large intestine

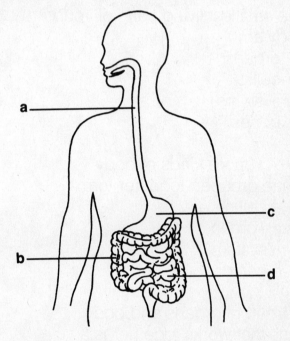

Short Essay   Write your answers in complete sentences.

15. Why does your body need to change food by
     digesting it?

The food must be changed into substances that body cells

can use. After the food is digested, the substances pass

into the blood and are carried to the body cells.

16. What might happen if you injured your spinal cord?

You might lose the ability to move parts of your body.

You might lose feeling in parts of your body.

Name _____

Multiple Choice   Choose the best answer.

1. The body's building blocks are
   a. cells.
   b. organs.
   c. tissues.
   d. systems.

2. An organ is made up of two or more kinds of
   a. systems.
   b. tissues.
   c. nerves.
   d. muscles.

3. Your pulse is caused by
   a. blood moving.
   b. air in your lungs.
   c. your arm muscles.
   d. digestive juices.

4. The heart and blood vessels are part of the
   a. circulatory system.
   b. digestive system.
   c. respiratory system.
   d. nervous system.

5. The blood gives off carbon dioxide and picks up oxygen in the
   a. muscles.
   b. arteries.
   c. heart.
   d. lungs.

6. The digestive system changes food so that the body gets needed
   a. carbon dioxide.
   b. tissues.
   c. nutrients.
   d. capillaries.

7. Lungs and air sacs are part of the
   a. digestive system.
   b. respiratory system.
   c. circulatory system.
   d. nervous system.

8. Motor nerves and sensory nerves are part of the
   a. nervous system.
   b. circulatory system.
   c. respiratory system.
   d. digestive system.

9. When you reach adult size, your bones
   a. stop growing.
   b. grow longer.
   c. grow heavier.
   d. become softer.

10. A body that works the way it should is always
    a. fast.
    b. big.
    c. strong.
    d. healthy.

Short Answer Use the diagram to answer the questions.
Write the correct letter in each blank.

b 11. This connects the nerves in
your body to your brain.

c 12. This kind of nerve carries
messages to your brain.

d 13. This kind of nerve carries
messages from your brain.

a 14. This organ gathers
information from your
senses.

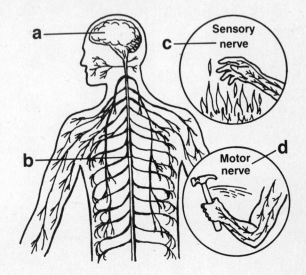

Short Essay Write your answers in complete sentences.

15. How do your circulatory system and your respiratory
system work together?

   Air sacs in the lungs fill with air when you breathe in.

   Oxygen from the air passes into blood vessels. The

   blood carries the oxygen to the heart and then to all

   body cells. Carbon dioxide passes out of the blood

   into the air sacs and is breathed out by the lungs.

16. What might happen if your brain did not help control
your breathing all the time?

   You would have to think about breathing all the time.

   You would not be able to breath when you sleep.

Multiple Choice   Choose the best answer.

1. Physical fitness helps you
   a. stay tired.
   b. stay healthy.
   c. make friends.
   d. become smarter.

2. Your muscles will get enough oxygen if you have healthy
   a. legs.
   b. lungs.
   c. arms.
   d. posture.

3. Your muscles can become weak when you
   a. do not exercise.
   b. eat healthy foods.
   c. sleep at night.
   d. argue with friends.

4. Endurance is the ability to
   a. lift heavy weights once.
   b. move the body easily.
   c. sit up straight.
   d. use muscles for a long time without tiring.

5. You can increase your flexibility by
   a. eating more food.
   b. lifting heavy weights.
   c. sleeping well at night.
   d. exercising.

6. The best fitness activities are ones that you
   a. find easy to do.
   b. find hard to do.
   c. have never done.
   d. enjoy doing.

7. Regular exercise can help make people
   a. relaxed and happy.
   b. taller.
   c. smarter.
   d. tired and grumpy.

8. Throwing and catching are
   a. competitive games.
   b. Project Keep-Fit exercises.
   c. sports skills.
   d. endurance exercises.

9. A sport that people can play all their lives is called a
   a. sports skill.
   b. lifetime sport.
   c. fitness exercise.
   d. team sport.

10. Games are the most fun when
    a. everyone is included.
    b. one person always wins.
    c. only the best players play.
    d. they are hard to play.

Short Answer   Match each meaning in Column I with the correct term in Column II.

Column I

_____ 11. The ability to use muscles for a long period of time

_____ 12. The ability of muscles to produce quite a bit of force

_____ 13. The way a person holds the body while sitting, standing, or walking

_____ 14. The ability of muscles to move easily and freely

Column II

a. posture

b. flexibility

c. muscle endurance

d. muscle strength

Short Essay   Write your answers in complete sentences.

15. Why is it important to have good posture?

_____

_____

_____

_____.

16. Is it most important for you to have strength, flexibility, or endurance? Explain your choice.

_____

_____

_____

_____.

Name _____

Multiple Choice   Choose the best answer.

1. Regular exercise is very helpful to your
   a. heart.
   b. blood.
   c. brain.
   d. stomach.

2. Healthy lungs can give your muscles needed
   a. blood.
   b. rest.
   c. oxygen.
   d. body fat.

3. One way to increase flexibility is to
   a. rest often.
   b. stand straight.
   c. lift heavy objects.
   d. stretch your muscles.

4. A person who can work for a long time without getting tired has
   a. flexibility.
   b. endurance.
   c. good posture.
   d. balance.

5. To build fitness you need to
   a. exercise longer and harder.
   b. work less.
   c. play less.
   d. play indoors.

6. If you choose fitness activities you enjoy, you will probably
   a. exercise regularly
   b. exercise less.
   c. become weaker.
   d. become tired.

7. Many people like to exercise because it helps them feel
   a. tired.
   b. important.
   c. relaxed.
   d. older.

8. Some sports skills are running, jumping, throwing, and
   a. lifting weights.
   b. pushups.
   c. leg-lifts.
   d. catching.

9. Sports skills are most useful for games such as
   a. checkers and puzzles.
   b. tic-tac-toe.
   c. word games.
   d. baseball and tennis.

10. Sports are most fun when
    a. there are no rules.
    b. everyone is included.
    c. no players are very skilled.
    d. only the best players are included.

Short Answer   Match each meaning in Column I with the correct term in Column II.

Column I   **Column II**

___ 11. the ability to exercise, play,   a. physical fitness
        and work without getting
        tired or injured easily

___ 12. the ability of muscles to   b. posture
        produce quite a bit of force

___ 13. the way you hold your body
        while standing, walking, or   c. warm-ups
        sitting

___ 14. exercises that get you ready
        for more active exercises   d. muscle strength

Short Essay   Write your answers in complete sentences.

15. Why are warm-up exercises important?

_____

_____

_____

_____.

16. Team sports use many skills. Choose one team sport
    and list three different skills used to play it.

_____

_____

_____.

Name _____

Multiple Choice   Choose the best answer.

1. Physical fitness helps you
   a. stay tired.
   (b.) stay healthy.
   c. make friends.
   d. become smarter.

2. Your muscles will get enough oxygen if you have healthy
   a. legs.
   (b.) lungs.
   c. arms.
   d. posture.

3. Your muscles can become weak when you
   (a.) do not exercise.
   b. eat healthy foods.
   c. sleep at night.
   d. argue with friends.

4. Endurance is the ability to
   a. lift heavy weights once.
   b. move the body easily.
   c. sit up straight.
   (d.) use muscles for a long time without tiring.

5. You can increase your flexibility by
   a. eating more food.
   b. lifting heavy weights.
   c. sleeping well at night.
   (d.) exercising.

6. The best fitness activities are ones that you
   a. find easy to do.
   b. find hard to do.
   c. have never done.
   (d.) enjoy doing.

7. Regular exercise can help make people
   (a.) relaxed and happy.
   b. taller.
   c. smarter.
   d. tired and grumpy.

8. Throwing and catching are
   a. competitive games.
   b. Project Keep-Fit exercises.
   (c.) sports skills.
   d. endurance exercises.

9. A sport that people can play all their lives is called a
   a. sports skill.
   (b.) lifetime sport.
   c. fitness exercise.
   d. team sport.

10. Games are the most fun when
    (a.) everyone is included.
    b. one person always wins.
    c. only the best players play.
    d. they are hard to play.

Short Answer   Match each meaning in Column I with the correct term in Column II.

Column I

<u>c</u> 11. The ability to use muscles for a long period of time

<u>d</u> 12. The ability of muscles to produce quite a bit of force

<u>a</u> 13. The way a person holds the body while sitting, standing, or walking

<u>b</u> 14. The ability of muscles to move easily and freely

Column II

a. posture

b. flexibility

c. muscle endurance

d. muscle strength

Short Essay   Write your answers in complete sentences.

15. Why is it important to have good posture?

    Good posture is part of endurance. With good

    posture, you hold your body in a balanced and

    comfortable way. You can sit, stand, or walk

    for a long time without feeling tired.

16. Is it most important for you to have strength, flexibility, or endurance? Explain your choice.

    Answers will vary, may include: strength, because

    it helps me play active sports; flexibility,

    because it helps me move easily without hurting

    my muscles; endurance, because it helps me ride

    my bike for a long time without getting tired.

Multiple Choice   Choose the best answer.

1. Regular exercise is very helpful
   to your
   a. heart.
   b. blood.
   c. brain.
   d. stomach.

2. Healthy lungs can give your
   muscles needed
   a. blood.
   b. rest.
   c. oxygen.
   d. body fat.

3. One way to increase flexibility is
   to
   a. rest often.
   b. stand straight.
   c. lift heavy objects.
   d. stretch your muscles.

4. A person who can work for a
   long time without getting tired
   has
   a. flexibility.
   b. endurance.
   c. good posture.
   d. balance.

5. To build fitness you need to
   a. exercise longer and harder.
   b. work less.
   c. play less.
   d. play indoors.

6. If you choose fitness activities
   you enjoy, you will probably
   a. exercise regularly.
   b. exercise less.
   c. become weaker.
   d. become tired.

7. Many people like to exercise
   because it helps them feel
   a. tired.
   b. important.
   c. relaxed.
   d. older.

8. Some sports skills are running,
   jumping, throwing, and
   a. lifting weights.
   b. pushups.
   c. leg-lifts.
   d. catching.

9. Sports skills are most useful for
   games such as
   a. checkers and puzzles.
   b. tic-tac-toe.
   c. word games.
   d. baseball and tennis.

10. Sports are most fun when
    a. there are no rules.
    b. everyone is included.
    c. no players are very skilled.
    d. only the best players are
       included.

Short Answer   Match each meaning in Column I with the correct term in Column II.

Column I

<u>a</u> 11. the ability to exercise, play, and work without getting tired or injured easily

<u>d</u> 12. the ability of muscles to produce quite a bit of force

<u>b</u> 13. the way you hold your body while standing, walking, or sitting

<u>c</u> 14. exercises that get you ready for more active exercises

Column II

a. physical fitness

b. posture

c. warm-ups

d. muscle strength

Short Essay   Write your answers in complete sentences.

15. Why are warm-up exercises important?

Warm-up exercises help stretch the muscles before a

person does more active exercises. They help prevent

muscle soreness and injury.

16. Team sports use many skills. Choose one team sport and list three different skills used to play it.

Answers will vary, may include: baseball—running,

throwing, and catching; volleyball—running, hitting

a ball, jumping.

Name _____

Multiple Choice   Choose the best answer.

1. Being a careful pedestrian means to
   a. walk safely.
   b. run safely.
   c. drive safely.
   d. be a jaywalker.

2. How should a careful pedestrian walk on a street that has no sidewalk?
   a. in the middle
   b. on the left side
   c. on the right side
   d. with the traffic flow

3. Safe bicycles are
   a. hard to ride.
   b. too high for the rider's feet to touch the ground.
   c. hard to stop.
   d. the right size for the rider.

4. All safe swimmers know
   a. where and when they can swim.
   b. many strokes.
   c. how to swim fast.
   d. how to rescue people.

5. The first thing to do when seeing someone in the water who needs to be rescued is
   a. call for help.
   b. jump in the water.
   c. keep calm and quiet.
   d. swim to the person.

6. The first thing to remember during an emergency is to
   a. run fast.
   b. stay calm.
   c. talk loudly.
   d. find out what happened.

7. Burns often cause
   a. deep cuts.
   b. bruises.
   c. blisters.
   d. marks on the body that look like scrapes.

8. A bandage put on a cut must always be
   a. large.
   b. small.
   c. white.
   d. clean.

9. If a stranger calls, a child who answers the phone when home alone should
   a. keep the door locked.
   b. get pencil and paper.
   c. not tell he or she is alone.
   d. go away.

10. Children who are home by themselves should have friends visiting
    a. for safety.
    b. only with parents' permission.
    c. whenever possible.
    d. in case strangers call.

Short Answer   Match each emergency in Column I with the correct first aid in Column II. Write the correct letter on the blank.

Column I

____ 11. A boat passenger falls overboard into the water

____ 12. A grown-up has suddenly become very sick

____ 13. Someone has gotten a mild burn

____ 14. Someone has broken a blister

Column II

a. Apply a cold, wet cloth and ice.

b. Wash with soap and water, then bandage.

c. Throw out a rope or something that floats.

d. Get help immediately.

Short Essay   Write your answers in complete sentences.

15. People who jaywalk can get hurt. How might they cause other people to get hurt, too?

_____

_____

_____

_____

16. What rule might help a parent know that children who are home alone are safe?

_____

_____

_____

Multiple Choice   Choose the best answer.

1. What should a careful pedestrian do before crossing a street?
   a. give a hand signal
   b. step off the curb
   c. face the cars
   d. look left, then right, then left again

2. What helps a person stay safe when walking outdoors at night?
   a. wearing loose-fitting clothing
   b. wearing light-colored clothing
   c. wearing tight-fitting clothing
   d. wearing dark-colored clothing

3. When a person rides a bicycle on the street, he or she must obey the rules for
   a. pedestrians.
   b. cars.
   c. parking.
   d. sidewalk bicycles.

4. The first step to being safe in the water is knowing how to
   a. swim.
   b. rescue someone.
   c. hold one's breath.
   d. dive.

5. When rescuing someone who is in the water, a person should first
   a. find out what has happened.
   b. swim to the person in trouble.
   c. yell for help.
   d. phone the police.

6. An emergency is a
   a. kind of first aid.
   b. rescue.
   c. sudden accident or illness.
   d. minor injury.

7. When a person has been hurt, the first help given is called
   a. an emergency.
   b. first aid.
   c. a rescue.
   d. an injury.

8. A blister can be caused by
   a. falling.
   b. a deep cut.
   c. a loose bandage.
   d. a burn.

9. When a person is home alone, he or she should never open the door to
   a. invited visitors.
   b. his or her parents.
   c. strangers.
   d. anyone.

10. What list is helpful to keep next to the family telephone?
    a. emergency telephone numbers
    b. first aid rules
    c. safety rules
    d. birthday dates of all family members

Short Answer   Match the beginning of each sentence in Column I with the correct ending in Column II. Write the correct letter on the blank.

Column I

_____ 11. If a person carries another person on a bicycle,

_____ 12. If a child swims where a parent or lifeguard can watch,

_____ 13. If a person stays calm in an emergency,

_____ 14. If families make lists of important telephone numbers,

Column II

a. help will be near in case of an emergency in the water.

b. the driver will not be able to steer and stop easily.

c. they will save time calling for help if they need it.

d. he or she will be able to think of how to help.

Short Essay   Write your answers in complete sentences.

15. Why does a careful pedestrian always look both ways before stepping off the curb, even if the traffic signal tells cars to stop?

_____

_____.

16. How does first aid for a cut help protect people from germs?

_____

_____

_____

_____.

Name _____

Multiple Choice   Choose the best answer.

1. Being a careful pedestrian means to
   a. walk safely.
   b. run safely.
   c. drive safely.
   d. be a jaywalker.

2. How should a careful pedestrian walk on a street that has no sidewalk?
   a. in the middle
   b. on the left side
   c. on the right side
   d. with the traffic flow

3. Safe bicycles are
   a. hard to ride.
   b. too high for the rider's feet to touch the ground.
   c. hard to stop.
   d. the right size for the rider.

4. All safe swimmers know
   a. where and when they can swim.
   b. many strokes.
   c. how to swim fast.
   d. how to rescue people.

5. The first thing to do when seeing someone in the water who needs to be rescued is
   a. call for help.
   b. jump in the water.
   c. keep calm and quiet.
   d. swim to the person.

6. The first thing to remember during an emergency is to
   a. run fast.
   b. stay calm.
   c. talk loudly.
   d. find out what happened.

7. Burns often cause
   a. deep cuts.
   b. bruises.
   c. blisters.
   d. marks on the body that look like scrapes.

8. A bandage put on a cut must always be
   a. large.
   b. small.
   c. white.
   d. clean.

9. If a stranger calls, a child who answers the phone when home alone should
   a. keep the door locked.
   b. get pencil and paper.
   c. not tell he or she is alone.
   d. go away.

10. Children who are home by themselves should have friends visiting
   a. for safety.
   b. only with parents' permission.
   c. whenever possible.
   d. in case strangers call.

Short Answer   Match each emergency in Column I with the correct first aid in Column II. Write the correct letter on the blank.

Column I

_c_ 11. A boat passenger falls overboard into the water.

_d_ 12. A grown-up has suddenly become very sick.

_a_ 13. Someone has gotten a mild burn.

_b_ 14. Someone has broken a blister.

Column II

a. Apply a cold, wet cloth and ice.

b. Wash with soap and water, then bandage.

c. Throw out a rope or something that floats.

d. Get help immediately.

Short Essay   Write your answers in complete sentences.

15. People who jaywalk can get hurt. How might they cause other people to get hurt, too?

   Drivers might have accidents trying to

   avoid jaywalkers. Jaywalkers might cause

   a car to hit another pedestrian when

   avoiding the jaywalker.

16. What rule might help a parent know that children who are home alone are safe?

   Answers might include: parents can leave a number

   where they may be reached; time limits on calls

   to friends, because parents may want to call home.

Multiple Choice   Choose the best answer.

1. What should a careful pedestrian do before crossing a street?
   a. give a hand signal
   b. step off the curb
   c. face the cars
   (d.) look left, then right, then left again

2. What helps a person stay safe when walking outdoors at night?
   a. wearing loose-fitting clothing
   (b.) wearing light-colored clothing
   c. wearing tight-fitting clothing
   d. wearing dark-colored clothing

3. When a person rides a bicycle on the street, he or she must obey the rules for
   a. pedestrians.
   (b.) cars.
   c. parking.
   d. sidewalk bicycles.

4. The first step to being safe in the water is knowing how to
   (a.) swim.
   b. rescue someone.
   c. hold one's breath.
   d. dive.

5. When rescuing someone who is in the water, a person should first
   a. find out what has happened.
   b. swim to the person in trouble.
   (c.) yell for help.
   d. phone the police.

6. An emergency is a
   a. kind of first aid.
   b. rescue.
   (c.) sudden accident or illness.
   d. minor injury.

7. When a person has been hurt, the first help given is called
   a. an emergency.
   (b.) first aid.
   c. a rescue.
   d. an injury.

8. A blister can be caused by
   a. falling.
   b. a deep cut.
   c. a loose bandage.
   (d.) a burn.

9. When a person is home alone, he or she should never open the door to
   a. invited visitors.
   b. his or her parents.
   (c.) strangers.
   d. anyone.

10. What list is helpful to keep next to the family telephone?
    (a.) emergency telephone numbers
    b. first aid rules
    c. safety rules
    d. birthday dates of all family members

Short Answer   Match the beginning of each sentence in Column I with the correct ending in Column II. Write the correct letter on the blank.

Column I

b 11. If a person carries another person on a bicycle,

a 12. If a child swims where a parent or lifeguard can watch,

d 13. If a person stays calm in an emergency,

c 14. If families make lists of important telephone numbers,

Column II

a. help will be near in case of an emergency in the water.

b. the driver will not be able to steer and stop easily.

c. they will save time calling for help if they need it.

d. he or she will be able to think of how to help.

Short Essay   Write your answers in complete sentences.

15. Why does a careful pedestrian always look both ways before stepping off the curb, even if the traffic signal tells cars to stop?

   The driver might not obey the traffic signal. Careful pedestrians

   make sure before entering the street that drivers will stop.

16. How does first aid for a cut help protect people from germs?

   A cut in the skin may let germs in. First aid destroys

   the germs on the surface of the skin by washing the

   cut. A clean bandage keeps germs in the air

   from entering the cut.

Multiple Choice   Choose the best answer.

1. While a person is sleeping, his or her body
   a. stops growing.
   b. is very warm.
   c. slows down its heart rate.
   d. cools off greatly.

2. How does a person feel who gets enough sleep at night?
   a. tired in the morning
   b. rested in the morning
   c. not able to think clearly.
   d. grouchy

3. Each tooth is held in the jaw by one or more
   a. roots.
   b. gums.
   c. crowns.
   d. incisors.

4. An orthodontist is a special kind of dentist who
   a. cleans teeth.
   b. straightens teeth.
   c. fills cavities.
   d. scrapes off plaque.

5. Gum disease can result from hardened plaque called
   a. enamel.
   b. dermis.
   c. cavities.
   d. calculus.

6. Skin helps a person cool off by
   a. stretching.
   b. producing sweat.
   c. making hairs stand up.
   d. shedding dead cells.

7. The nerve endings in the dermis
   a. produce sweat.
   b. send messages to the brain.
   c. cause hair to grow.
   d. keep the skin soft.

8. If a person has red, itchy eyes, what should he or she do?
   a. rub the eyes
   b. tell a parent or the school nurse
   c. ignore it
   d. wash the eyes

9. What does a person need when he or she buys a health-care product?
   a. a lot of money
   b. information about the health-care products
   c. advice from a friend
   d. a list of available products

10. Which of the following questions can best help someone decide if a health-care product is right for his or her use?
    a. Does a famous person use it?
    b. What can the product do?
    c. Does it have a nice package?
    d. Who makes the product?

Short Answer   Complete the chart.

Description	Part
hold teeth in the jaw	roots
11.	incisor
tooth with two points	12.
one-pointed, tearing tooth	13.
14.	molar
outer layer of skin	15.
16.	pore
lower layer of skin	17.

Short Essay   Write your answers in complete sentences.

18. When the dentist looks into the mouth of a nine-year-old, what things might he or she be looking for?

    _____

    _____

    _____

    _____ .

19. Why is a television commercial a poor source of information about a health-care product?

    _____

    _____ .

Name _____

Multiple Choice   Choose the best answer.

1. When a person is asleep
   a. the brain sends fewer messages to the muscles.
   b. the body shuts down.
   c. the heart beats more quickly.
   d. the lungs stop working.

2. Why is enough sleep important to children?
   a. It keeps them safe.
   b. It strengthens their muscles.
   c. It helps them grow and learn properly.
   d. It improves their self-image.

3. Which teeth have two points and one or two roots?
   a. molars
   b. cuspids
   c. incisors
   d. bicuspids

4. The first teeth a person gets are called
   a. permanent teeth.
   b. primary teeth.
   c. molars.
   d. bicuspids.

5. Calculus forms on the gumline when
   a. cavities grow.
   b. primary teeth fall out.
   c. plaque hardens.
   d. permanent teeth grow in crooked.

6. Sweat leaves the body through small openings in the skin called
   a. pores.
   b. dermis.
   c. epidermis.
   d. incisors.

7. The dermis is under the
   a. pores.
   b. nerve endings.
   c. skin.
   d. epidermis.

8. What should a person do who has an earache?
   a. go to sleep
   b. tell a parent or nurse
   c. ignore it
   d. clean the ears

9. Where can someone find the best information about a health-care product?
   a. from an ad featuring a famous person
   b. in the newspaper
   c. from a television commercial
   d. on the product label

10. What information should a person always read on the label of a health product?
   a. who uses the product
   b. where the product is made
   c. the weight of the package
   d. how to use the product

Short Answer   Use the pictures to identify the parts.
Write the correct letter on each blank.

____ 11. bicuspid

____ 12. gum

____ 13. cuspid

____ 14. root

____ 15. incisor

____ 16. molar

____ 17. crown

Short Essay   Write your answer in complete sentences.

18. Jeff is nine years old. He has been getting twelve
     hours of sleep each night for the last five years. How
     could Jeff know if he still needs that much sleep?

     _____

     _____

     _____

     _____ .

19. Tina's hair is very dry and her scalp is itchy. How can
     she choose a good shampoo for her needs?

     _____

     _____

     _____

Multiple Choice Choose the best answer.

1. While a person is sleeping, his or her body
   a. stops growing.
   b. is very warm.
   (c.) slows down its heart rate.
   d. cools off greatly.

2. How does a person feel who gets enough sleep at night?
   a. tired in the morning
   (b.) rested in the morning
   c. not able to think clearly
   d. grouchy

3. Each tooth is held in the jaw by one or more
   (a.) roots.
   b. gums.
   c. crowns.
   d. incisors.

4. An orthodontist is a special kind of dentist who
   a. cleans teeth.
   (b.) straightens teeth.
   c. fills cavities.
   d. scrapes off plaque.

5. Gum disease can result from hardened plaque called
   a. enamel.
   b. dermis.
   c. cavities.
   (d.) calculus.

6. Skin helps a person cool off by
   a. stretching.
   (b.) producing sweat.
   c. making hairs stand up.
   d. shedding dead cells.

7. The nerve endings in the dermis
   a. produce sweat.
   (b.) send messages to the brain.
   c. cause hair to grow.
   d. keep the skin soft.

8. If a person has red, itchy eyes, what should he or she do?
   a. rub the eyes
   (b.) tell a parent or the school nurse
   c. ignore it
   d. wash the eyes

9. What does a person need when he or she buys a health-care product?
   a. a lot of money
   (b.) information about the health-care products
   c. advice from a friend
   d. a list of available products

10. Which of the following questions can best help someone decide if a health-care product is right for his or her use?
    a. Does a famous person use it?
    (b.) What can the product do?
    c. Does it have a nice package?
    d. Who makes the product?

Short Answer Complete the chart.

Description	Part
hold teeth in the jaw	roots
11. **tooth used to cut food**	incisor
tooth with two points	12. **bicuspid**
one-pointed, tearing tooth	13. **cuspid**
14. **tooth used to grind food**	molar
outer layer of skin	15. **epidermis**
16. **small opening in the skin**	pore
lower layer of skin	17. **dermis**

Short Essay Write your answers in complete sentences.

18. When the dentist looks into the mouth of a nine-year-old, what things might he or she be looking for?

    Answers might include: cavities, plaque, calculus,

    gum disease; to see if primary teeth are

    falling out at the right time and if permanent

    teeth are growing in straight.

19. Why is a television commercial a poor source of information about a health-care product?

    Information in commercials is designed to sell

    a product. A consumer needs better facts.

Multiple Choice   Choose the best answer.

1. When a person is asleep
   a. the brain sends fewer
      messages to the muscles.
   b. the body shuts down.
   c. the heart beats more quickly.
   d. the lungs stop working.

2. Why is enough sleep important
   to children?
   a. It keeps them out of trouble.
   b. It strengthens their muscles.
   c. It helps them grow
      and learn properly.
   d. It improves their self-image.

3. Which teeth have two points and
   one or two roots?
   a. molars
   b. cuspids
   c. incisors
   d. bicuspids

4. The first teeth a person gets are
   called
   a. permanent teeth.
   b. primary teeth.
   c. molars.
   d. bicuspids.

5. Calculus forms on the gumline
   when
   a. cavities grow.
   b. primary teeth fall out.
   c. plaque hardens.
   d. permanent teeth grow in
      crooked.

6. Sweat leaves the body through
   small openings in the skin
   called
   a. pores.
   b. dermis.
   c. epidermis.
   d. incisors.

7. The dermis is under the
   a. pores.
   b. nerve endings.
   c. skin.
   d. epidermis.

8. What should a person do who
   has an earache?
   a. go to sleep
   b. tell a parent or nurse
   c. ignore it
   d. clean the ears

9. Where can someone find the
   best information about a
   health-care product?
   a. from an ad featuring a
      famous person
   b. in the newspaper
   c. from a television commercial
   d. on the product label

10. What information should a
    person always read on the label
    of a health product?
    a. who uses the product
    b. where the product is made
    c. the weight of the package
    d. how to use the product

Short Answer   Use the pictures to identify the parts.
Write the correct letter on each blank.

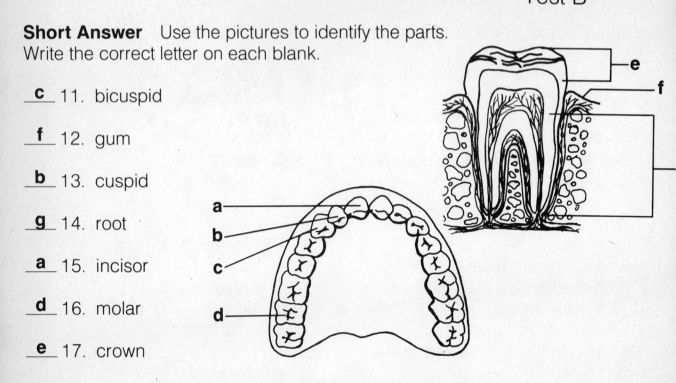

__c__ 11. bicuspid

__f__ 12. gum

__b__ 13. cuspid

__g__ 14. root

__a__ 15. incisor

__d__ 16. molar

__e__ 17. crown

Short Essay   Write your answer in complete sentences.

18. Jeff is nine years old. He has been getting twelve
    hours of sleep each night for the last five years. How
    could Jeff know if he still needs that much sleep?

    Jeff can ask himself if he feels tired during the day or

    has trouble concentrating on what he is doing. If not,

    he could suggest getting only 11 hours of sleep

    which is average for his age.

19. Tina's hair is very dry and her scalp is itchy. How can
    she choose a good shampoo for her needs?

    Answers might include: talk to parents or the school

    nurse; talk with friends who have the same problem;

    read product labels; read magazine articles.

Multiple Choice Choose the best answer.

1. An empty stomach sends a message about hunger to the
   a. mouth.
   b. hands.
   c. brain.
   d. heart.

2. People who want to keep healthy need to eat
   a. only one kind of food.
   b. different kinds of food.
   c. as much meat as possible.
   d. many kinds of cookies.

3. Proteins, carbohydrates, and fats are three kinds of
   a. food groups.
   b. minerals.
   c. vitamins.
   d. nutrients.

4. The meat-poultry-fish-bean food group includes
   a. oatmeal.
   b. chicken.
   c. butter.
   d. cheese.

5. The bread-cereal food group includes
   a. rice.
   b. fruit juice.
   c. cheese.
   d. chicken.

6. Rickets and scurvy are diseases that people develop when they do not get enough of some
   a. minerals.
   b. vitamins.
   c. fats.
   d. meats.

7. Vitamin C is in
   a. lemons.
   b. rice.
   c. chicken.
   d. eggs.

8. One healthy eating habit would be to limit
   a. milk and cheese.
   b. meat and beans.
   c. some sugar, salt, and fat.
   d. bread and cereal.

9. What can grow in food and spoil it?
   a. carbohydrates
   b. salt
   c. minerals
   d. bacteria

10. Before preparing food, people should always
    a. wash their hands.
    b. make sure they are hungry.
    c. cover the food.
    d. freeze the food.

Short Answer   Each meal in Column I is missing a food from one food group. Tell which food group from Column II is missing. Write the correct letter on the blank.

Column I

___ 11. oatmeal, grapefruit juice, a slice of ham

___ 12. bean salad with tomato, cottage cheese

___ 13. a peanut butter sandwich, yogurt

___ 14. tomato juice, a Swiss cheese sandwich

Column II

a. vegetable-fruit group

b. bread-cereal group

c. milk-cheese group

d. meat-poultry-fish-bean group

Short Essay   Write your answers in complete sentences.

15. How can a person plan three healthy meals a day?

_____

_____

_____

_____

16. What could sailors in the late 1800s have eaten instead of lemon juice to prevent scurvy? Why?

_____

_____

_____

Multiple Choice   Choose the best answer.

1. How long after eating a meal do people have food in their stomachs?
   a. about thirty minutes
   b. about one hour
   c. about four hours
   d. about ten hours

2. Proteins and vitamins are two kinds of
   a. minerals.
   b. foods.
   c. nutrients.
   d. vegetables.

3. How often do people need to eat foods from each food group?
   a. once a week
   b. every day
   c. only when sick
   d. once every three days

4. Tuna fish is in the
   a. vegetable-fruit group.
   b. bread-cereal group.
   c. milk-cheese group.
   d. meat-poultry-fish-bean group.

5. In 1919, doctors learned that rickets was caused by a lack of
   a. carbohydrates.
   b. protein.
   c. vitamin C.
   d. vitamin D.

6. The British navy prevented scurvy by giving sailors
   a. salty foods.
   b. milk.
   c. lemon juice.
   d. more sleep at night.

7. Trying new foods helps people eat
   a. only foods they like.
   b. a variety of foods.
   c. large amounts of food.
   d. less food.

8. People can get sick if they eat foods spoiled by
   a. bacteria.
   b. minerals.
   c. salt.
   d. carbohydrates.

9. Where should cheese be stored to prevent it from spoiling?
   a. on a shelf
   b. on the counter
   c. in a bread box
   d. in the refrigerator

10. Washing fresh vegetables before they are served removes
    a. bacteria, dirt, and chemicals.
    b. proteins and vitamins.
    c. the color.
    d. the skin.

Short Answer   Each meal in Column I is missing a food from one food group. Tell which food group from Column II is missing. Write the correct letter on the blank.

Column I

____ 11. fish, cornbread, melon

____ 12. chicken, fresh broccoli, an apple, a glass of milk

____ 13. tuna fish, Swiss cheese, and rye bread sandwich

____ 14. peas and carrots with rice, a glass of milk

Column II

a. vegetable-fruit group

b. bread-cereal group

c. milk-cheese group

d. meat-poultry-fish-bean group

Short Essay   Write your answers in complete sentences.

15. How might food help a person who is often tired and unhappy?

_____

_____

_____

16. What would a community food inspector look for in a restaurant to make sure it is clean?

_____

_____

_____

_____

Name _____

Multiple Choice   Choose the best answer.

1. An empty stomach sends a
   message about hunger to
   the
   a. mouth.
   b. hands.
   c. brain.
   d. heart.

2. People who want to keep
   healthy need to eat
   a. only one kind of food.
   b. different kinds of food.
   c. as much meat as possible.
   d. many kinds of cookies.

3. Proteins, carbohydrates, and fats
   are three kinds of
   a. food groups.
   b. minerals.
   c. vitamins.
   d. nutrients.

4. The meat-poultry-fish-bean food
   group includes
   a. oatmeal.
   b. chicken.
   c. butter.
   d. cheese.

5. The bread-cereal food group
   includes
   a. rice.
   b. fruit juice.
   c. cheese.
   d. chicken.

6. Rickets and scurvy are diseases
   that people develop when they
   do not get enough of some
   a. minerals.
   b. vitamins.
   c. fats.
   d. meats.

7. Vitamin C is in
   a. lemons.
   b. rice.
   c. chicken.
   d. eggs.

8. One healthy eating habit would
   be to limit
   a. milk and cheese.
   b. meat and beans.
   c. sugar, salt, and fat.
   d. bread and cereal.

9. What can grow in food and
   spoil it?
   a. carbohydrates
   b. salt
   c. minerals
   d. bacteria

10. Before preparing food, people
    should always
    a. wash their hands.
    b. make sure they are hungry.
    c. cover the food.
    d. freeze the food.

Short Answer   Each meal in Column I is missing a food from one food group. Tell which food group from Column II is missing. Write the correct letter on the blank.

Column I

Column II

_c_ 11. oatmeal, grapefruit juice,
a slice of ham

_b_ 12. bean salad with tomato,
cottage cheese

_a_ 13. a peanut butter sandwich,
yogurt

_d_ 14. tomato juice, a Swiss
cheese sandwich

a. vegetable-fruit group

b. bread-cereal group

c. milk-cheese group

d. meat-poultry-fish-bean group

Short Essay   Write your answers in complete sentences.

15. How can a person plan three healthy meals a day?

Answers might include: meals should include foods from

each food group; with at least four servings from the

fruit-vegetable group, four from the bread-cereal group,

three from the milk group, and two from the meat group.

16. What could sailors in the late 1800s have eaten
instead of lemon juice to prevent scurvy? Why?

Answers might include: any foods with vitamin C,

such as broccoli, citrus fruits, potatoes, peppers, and

strawberries. Vitamin C prevents scurvy.

Name _____

Multiple Choice   Choose the best answer.

1. How long after eating a meal do people have food in their stomachs?
   a. about thirty minutes
   b. about one hour
   (c.) about four hours
   d. about ten hours

2. Proteins and vitamins are two kinds of
   a. minerals.
   b. foods.
   (c.) nutrients.
   d. vegetables.

3. How often do people need to eat foods from each food group?
   a. once a week
   (b.) every day
   c. only when sick
   d. once every three days

4. Tuna fish is in the
   a. vegetable-fruit group.
   b. bread-cereal group.
   c. milk-cheese group.
   (d.) meat-poultry-fish-bean group.

5. In 1919, doctors learned that rickets was caused by a lack of
   a. carbohydrates.
   b. protein.
   c. vitamin C.
   (d.) vitamin D.

6. The British navy prevented scurvy by giving sailors
   a. salty foods.
   b. milk.
   (c.) lemon juice.
   d. more sleep at night.

7. Trying new foods helps people eat
   a. only foods they like.
   (b.) a variety of foods.
   c. large amounts of food.
   d. less food.

8. People can get sick if they eat foods spoiled by
   (a.) bacteria.
   b. minerals.
   c. salt.
   d. carbohydrates.

9. Where should cheese be stored to prevent it from spoiling?
   a. on a shelf
   b. on the counter
   c. in a bread box
   (d.) in the refrigerator

10. Washing fresh vegetables before they are served removes
    (a.) bacteria, dirt, and chemicals.
    b. proteins and vitamins.
    c. the color.
    d. the skin.

Short Answer   Each meal in Column I is missing a food from one food group. Tell which food group from Column II is missing. Write the correct letter on the blank.

Column I	Column II
_c_ 11. fish, cornbread, melon	a. vegetable-fruit group
_b_ 12. chicken, fresh broccoli, an apple, a glass of milk	b. bread-cereal group
_a_ 13. tuna fish, Swiss cheese, and rye bread sandwich	c. milk-cheese group
_d_ 14. peas and carrots with rice, a glass of milk	d. meat-poultry-fish-bean group

Short Essay   Write your answers in complete sentences.

15. How might food help a person who is often tired and unhappy?

Eating healthy meals with the proper foods from

all of the food groups can give a person energy

and even make him or her feel happier.

16. What would a community food inspector look for in a restaurant to make sure it is clean?

He or she would see if workers wash their

hands; if fruits and vegetables are washed;

if dishes, knives, forks, and spoons are

clean; and if foods are stored properly.

Multiple Choice Choose the best answer.

1. A drug
   a. is always useful.
   b. causes changes in the body.
   c. cannot be harmful.
   d. affects everyone the same way.

2. Over-the-counter medicines are used most often for
   a. a stuffy nose.
   b. diabetes.
   c. cancer.
   d. a heart problem.

3. Unwanted changes in the body that sometimes occur when taking medicines are called
   a. side effects.
   b. cures.
   c. abuse.
   d. diseases.

4. A doctor's order for a medicine is
   a. a label.
   b. an over-the-counter order.
   c. a safety-cap.
   d. a prescription.

5. Smoke from cigarettes can harm the lungs of
   a. smokers only.
   b. nonsmokers only.
   c. smokers and nonsmokers.
   d. no one.

6. Drinking small amounts of alcohol
   a. will not affect a young person.
   b. makes the mind clearer.
   c. will not affect an adult.
   d. can affect a person's thinking and coordination.

7. Marijuana is
   a. a harmful gas.
   b. a plant.
   c. the same as nicotine.
   d. a harmful liquid

8. Marijuana can cause changes that
   a. are harmless to the body.
   b. are harmful to the body.
   c. affect only young people.
   d. help people think clearly.

9. Paint thinners and glue
   a. are drugs.
   b. should always be stored in open jars.
   c. can be abused.
   d. should not be used in the house.

10. A person can best avoid abusing a drug by
    a. saying no to the offer of a drug.
    b. never using any kind of prescription medicine.
    c. reading drug labels.
    d. using only over-the-counter medicines.

Short Answer   Match each substance in Column I with the correct word or words in Column II. Write the correct letter on the blank. Some letters may be used more than once.

Column I

____ 11. over-the-counter drugs
____ 12. cocaine
____ 13. beer
____ 14. cigarettes
____ 15. wine
____ 16. tea
____ 17. cigars
____ 18. marijuana
____ 19. paint thinner
____ 20. gasoline

Column II

a. a drug that speeds up the heart
b. alcohol
c. harmful gases
d. contains hundreds of different drugs
e. usually used for health reasons
f. nicotine

Short Essay   Write your answers in complete sentences.

21. What should a young person do about a headache?

_____

_____

_____

_____ .

22. Mr. and Mrs. Simon have been married for twenty-eight years. Mr. Simon has smoked all those years. How might Mrs. Simon's health be affected?

_____

_____

_____ .

Multiple Choice   Choose the best answer.

1. All drugs are substances that
   a. a person eats or drinks.
   b. help a person keep healthy.
   c. cause changes in the body.
   d. are taken in pill form.

2. Prescription medicines
   a. can only be gotten with a doctor's order.
   b. always cause bad side effects.
   c. are always the same for everyone in a family.
   d. are the only drugs people abuse.

3. A person who has a side effect from a medicine
   a. has used a spoiled drug.
   b. has abused the medicine.
   c. will have a stomachache.
   d. should stop using the drug and call a doctor.

4. Aspirin is
   a. harmful to most people.
   b. an over-the-counter medicine.
   c. always needed for a headache.
   d. a prescription medicine.

5. A harmful drug in cigarettes and chewing tobacco is
   a. nicotine.
   b. aspirin.
   c. cocaine.
   d. alcohol.

6. Alcohol is a drug that usually
   a. affects a young person more quickly than an adult.
   b. affects an adult more quickly than a young person.
   c. does not affect adults.
   d. reaches the brain slowly.

7. The drugs in marijuana affect
   a. only the lungs.
   b. everyone in the same way.
   c. only young people.
   d. different people in different ways.

8. Marijuana
   a. contains many harmful substances.
   b. is an over-the-counter drug.
   c. is less harmful than cigarettes.
   d. is found in cola.

9. Paint thinners can be safe when used
   a. in a closed room.
   b. by an adult.
   c. according to instructions.
   d. by someone wearing gloves.

10. If a friend asks you to try a drug,
    a. say no.
    b. say nothing.
    c. take it, but do not use it.
    d. make sure it is a prescription medicine.

Short Answer   Read the list of descriptions. Tell whether it describes cocaine (C), nicotine (N), alcohol (A), or marijuana (M). Write the correct letter on the blank. Some answers may consist of more than one letter.

Descriptions

_____ 11. can cause heart attacks and brain seizures

_____ 12. damages the liver

_____ 13. found in beer and wine

_____ 14. can cause heart and lung diseases

_____ 15. found in chewing tobacco

_____ 16. can harm the lungs when smoked

_____ 17. can make people feel tired

_____ 18. can be abused

_____ 19. makes learning harder

_____ 20. affects a person's thinking

Short Essay   Write your answers in complete sentences.

21. Why should a person never use a prescription medicine meant for someone else?

_____

_____

_____

_____.

22. Mr. Washington learned that cigarette smoking is unhealthy, so he switched to pipes. What is wrong with his decision?

_____

_____

_____

_____.

Name _____

Multiple Choice   Choose the best answer.

1. A drug
    a. is always useful.
    b. causes changes in the body. (circled)
    c. cannot be harmful.
    d. affects everyone the same
        way.

2. Over-the-counter medicines are
    used most often for
    a. a stuffy nose. (circled)
    b. diabetes.
    c. cancer.
    d. a heart problem.

3. Unwanted changes in the body
    that sometimes occur when
    taking medicines are called
    a. side effects. (circled)
    b. cures.
    c. abuse.
    d. diseases.

4. A doctor's order for a medicine
    is
    a. a label.
    b. an over-the-counter order.
    c. a safety-cap.
    d. a prescription. (circled)

5. Smoke from cigarettes can harm
    the lungs of
    a. smokers only.
    b. nonsmokers only.
    c. smokers and nonsmokers. (circled)
    d. no one.

6. Drinking small amounts of
    alcohol
    a. will not affect a young
        person.
    b. makes the mind clearer.
    c. will not affect an adult.
    d. can affect a person's thinking (circled)
        and coordination.

7. Marijuana is
    a. a harmful gas.
    b. a plant. (circled)
    c. the same as nicotine.
    d. a harmful liquid.

8. Marijuana can cause changes
    that
    a. are harmless to the body.
    b. are harmful to the body. (circled)
    c. affect only young people.
    d. help people think clearly.

9. Paint thinners and glue
    a. are drugs.
    b. should always be stored in
        open jars.
    c. can be abused. (circled)
    d. should not be used in the
        house.

10. A person can best avoid abusing
    a drug by
    a. saying no to the offer of a (circled)
        drug.
    b. never using any kind of
        prescription medicine.
    c. reading drug labels.
    d. using only over-the-counter
        medicines.

Short Answer Match each substance in Column I with the correct word or words in Column II. Write the correct letter on the blank. Some letters may be used more than once.

Column I	Column II
_e_ 11. over-the-counter drugs	a. a drug that speeds up the heart
_a_ 12. cocaine	b. alcohol
_b_ 13. beer	c. harmful gases
_f_ 14. cigarettes	d. contains hundreds of different
_b_ 15. wine	drugs
_a_ 16. tea	e. usually used for health reasons
_f_ 17. cigars	f. nicotine
_d_ 18. marijuana	
_c_ 19. paint thinner	
_c_ 20. gasoline	

Short Essay Write your answers in complete sentences.

21. What should a young person do about a headache?

    Tell an adult. Try something other than

    medicine, such as rest, food, or mild activity.

    If headache continues, adult will decide to

    notify a doctor or give medicine.

22. Mr. and Mrs. Simon have been married for twenty-eight years. Mr. Simon has smoked all those years. How might Mrs. Simon's health be affected?

    She might have damaged lungs from breathing in

    his smoke. Her eyes may get watery or burn. The

    smoke may also cause her to cough and sneeze.

Multiple Choice   Choose the best answer.

1. All drugs are substances that
   a. a person eats or drinks.
   b. help a person keep healthy.
   c. cause changes in the body.
   d. are taken in pill form.

2. Prescription medicines
   a. can only be gotten with a doctor's order.
   b. always cause bad side effects.
   c. are always the same for everyone in a family.
   d. are the only drugs people abuse.

3. A person who has a side effect from a medicine
   a. has used a spoiled drug.
   b. has abused the medicine.
   c. will have a stomachache.
   d. should stop using the drug and call a doctor.

4. Aspirin is
   a. harmful to most people.
   b. an over-the-counter medicine.
   c. always needed for a headache.
   d. a prescription medicine.

5. A harmful drug in cigarettes and chewing tobacco is
   a. nicotine.
   b. aspirin.
   c. cocaine.
   d. alcohol.

6. Alcohol is a drug that usually
   a. affects a young person more quickly than an adult.
   b. affects an adult more quickly than a young person.
   c. does not affect adults.
   d. reaches the brain slowly.

7. The drugs in marijuana affect
   a. only the lungs.
   b. everyone in the same way.
   c. only young people.
   d. different people in different ways.

8. Marijuana
   a. contains many harmful substances.
   b. is an over-the-counter drug.
   c. is less harmful than cigarettes.
   d. is found in cola.

9. Paint thinners can be safe when used
   a. in a closed room.
   b. by an adult.
   c. according to instructions.
   d. by someone wearing gloves.

10. If a friend asks you to try a drug,
   a. say no.
   b. say nothing.
   c. take it, but do not use it.
   d. make sure it is a prescription medicine.

Short Answer   Read the list of descriptions. Tell whether it describes cocaine (C), nicotine (N), alcohol (A), or marijuana (M). Write the correct letter on the blank. Some answers may consist of more than one letter.

Descriptions

C _____ 11. can cause heart attacks and brain seizures
A _____ 12. damages the liver
A _____ 13. found in beer and wine
N _____ 14. can cause heart and lung diseases
N _____ 15. found in chewing tobacco
N,M _____ 16. can harm the lungs when smoked
N,A,M,C 17. can make people feel tired
C,N,A,M 18. can be abused
C,M,A _____ 19. makes learning harder
A,M,C _____ 20. affects a person's thinking

Short Essay   Write your answers in complete sentences.

21. Why should a person never use a prescription medicine meant for someone else?

A prescription medicine causes major

changes in the body. It is meant only

for the person it is written for.

22. Mr. Washington learned that cigarette smoking is unhealthy, so he switched to pipes. What is wrong with his decision?

Mr. Washington should quit smoking altogether.

Tobacco in pipes can cause the same health

problems caused by cigarettes which can harm

him and others.

Multiple Choice   Choose the best answer.

1. Communicable diseases are
caused by disease
   a. vaccines.
   b. germs.
   c. allergies.
   d. antibodies.

2. When disease germs are inside
the body, they
   a. try to get out.
   b. cannot live.
   c. grow larger.
   d. make more of themselves.

3. Bacteria and viruses are two
kinds of
   a. germs.
   b. diseases.
   c. measles.
   d. allergies.

4. AIDS is caused by a virus
that can kill
   a. certain white blood cells.
   b. viruses.
   c. bacteria.
   d. antibodies.

5. A medicine that causes the body
to produce antibodies is
   a. a vaccine.
   b. an antibiotic.
   c. an allergy.
   d. insulin.

6. What is a good way to
help prevent cardiovascular
disease?
   a. exercise
   b. bathe often
   c. take antibiotics
   d. receive vaccinations

7. The disease atherosclerosis
affects the
   a. liver.
   b. lungs.
   c. joints.
   d. arteries.

8. A person whose body does not
make enough insulin has
   a. arthritis.
   b. diabetes.
   c. cancer.
   d. allergies.

9. Cancer cells are
   a. bacteria.
   b. body cells that grow out of
control.
   c. antibodies.
   d. fatty substances.

10. Eating fewer sugary foods helps
protect a person's
   a. white blood cells.
   b. teeth.
   c. immunity.
   d. antibodies.

Short Answer Match each meaning in Column I with the correct word or words in Column II. Write the correct letter on the blank.

Column I

_____ 11. resistance to disease

_____ 12. a disease that causes a person to be bothered by certain foods, plants, dust, chemicals, or animal hair

_____ 13. any disease that cannot be passed from person to person

_____ 14. a disease that causes pain in the body's joints

Column II

a. immunity

b. noncommunicable disease

c. allergy

d. arthritis

Short Essay Write your answers in complete sentences.

15. If a person catches a cold, he or she may not feel sick until the next day. What has happened to the germs?

_____

_____.

16. When a person has a cold, how does the blood work to make him or her feel better?

_____

_____

_____

_____.

Multiple Choice   Choose the best answer.

1. All diseases that are caused by germs and spread are
   a. colds.
   b. communicable.
   c. viruses.
   d. noncommunicable.

2. Disease germs create more of themselves when they are in
   a. the air.
   b. the body.
   c. soap and water.
   d. cold, dry places.

3. Washing hands with soap and water can help
   a. prevent colds.
   b. cure colds.
   c. spread colds.
   d. keep germs in the air.

4. The body's blood helps fight germs with white blood cells and
   a. cilia.
   b. mucus.
   c. vaccines.
   d. antibodies.

5. A vaccine gives protection from certain germs by helping the body
   a. get a fever.
   b. get better after a cold.
   c. make antibodies.
   d. make antibiotics.

6. Cardiovascular diseases affect the
   a. heart.
   b. lungs.
   c. nose.
   d. throat.

7. Fatty substances blocking the arteries cause
   a. arthritis.
   b. antibiotics.
   c. atherosclerosis.
   d. flu.

8. Body cells that grow out of control and destroy other cells cause
   a. diabetes.
   b. cancer.
   c. antibodies.
   d. allergies.

9. A cure for the disease arthritis is
   a. eating fewer sweets and fatty foods.
   b. vaccines.
   c. antibiotics.
   d. not known yet.

10. Good health habits help prevent
    a. only communicable diseases.
    b. only heart diseases.
    c. allergies.
    d. both communicable and noncommunicable diseases.

Short Answer Write a C before each communicable disease and an N before each noncommunicable disease.

___ 11. disease caused by a virus

___ 12. disease that can be prevented by a vaccine

___ 13. cardiovascular disease

___ 14. allergies

___ 15. diabetes

Short Essay Write your answers in complete sentences.

16. Why do antibiotics help the body fight some diseases but not flu?

_____

_____

17. How does the AIDS virus damage the body?

_____

_____

_____

18. What eating habits are important to a healthy lifestyle?

_____

_____

_____

Name _____

Multiple Choice Choose the best answer.

1. Communicable diseases are caused by disease
   a. vaccines.
   b. germs.
   c. allergies.
   d. antibodies.

2. When disease germs are inside the body, they
   a. try to get out.
   b. cannot live.
   c. grow larger.
   d. make more of themselves.

3. Bacteria and viruses are two kinds of
   a. germs.
   b. diseases.
   c. measles.
   d. allergies.

4. AIDS is caused by a virus that can kill
   a. certain white blood cells.
   b. viruses.
   c. bacteria.
   d. antibodies.

5. A medicine that causes the body to produce antibodies is
   a. a vaccine.
   b. an antibiotic.
   c. an allergy.
   d. insulin.

6. What is a good way to help prevent cardiovascular disease?
   a. exercise
   b. bathe often
   c. take antibiotics
   d. receive vaccinations

7. The disease atherosclerosis affects the
   a. liver.
   b. lungs.
   c. joints.
   d. arteries.

8. A person whose body does not make enough insulin has
   a. arthritis.
   b. diabetes.
   c. cancer.
   d. allergies.

9. Cancer cells are
   a. bacteria.
   b. body cells that grow out of control.
   c. antibodies.
   d. fatty substances.

10. Eating fewer sugary foods helps protect a person's
    a. white blood cells.
    b. teeth.
    c. immunity.
    d. antibodies.

Short Answer   Match each meaning in Column I with the correct word or words in Column II. Write the correct letter on the blank.

Column I

_a_ 11. resistance to disease

_c_ 12. a disease that causes a person to be bothered by certain foods, plants, dust, chemicals, or animal hair

_b_ 13. any disease that cannot be passed from person to person

_d_ 14. a disease that causes pain in the body's joints

Column II

a. immunity

b. noncommunicable disease

c. allergy

d. arthritis

Short Essay   Write your answers in complete sentences.

15. If a person catches a cold, he or she may not feel sick until the next day. What has happened to the germs?

   More germs have been growing inside the body until

   there are so many that the person begins to feel sick.

16. When a person has a cold, how does the blood work to make him or her feel better?

   The blood carries white blood cells that attack

   disease germs. The blood also makes antibodies

   for each kind of disease. Antibodies attach to

   germs that cause the cold and make them harmless.

Multiple Choice   Choose the best answer.

1. All diseases that are caused by
   germs and spread are
   a. colds.
   (b.) communicable.
   c. viruses.
   d. noncommunicable.

2. Disease germs create more
   of themselves when they are
   in
   a. the air.
   (b.) the body.
   c. soap and water.
   d. cold, dry places.

3. Washing hands with soap and
   water can help
   (a.) prevent colds.
   b. cure colds.
   c. spread colds.
   d. keep germs in the air.

4. The body's blood helps fight
   germs with white blood cells
   and
   a. cilia.
   b. mucus.
   c. vaccines.
   (d.) antibodies.

5. A vaccine gives protection from
   certain germs by helping the
   body
   a. get a fever.
   b. get better after a cold.
   (c.) make antibodies.
   d. make antibiotics.

6. Cardiovascular diseases affect
   the
   (a.) heart.
   b. lungs.
   c. nose.
   d. throat.

7. Fatty substances blocking the
   arteries cause
   a. arthritis.
   b. antibiotics.
   (c.) atherosclerosis.
   d. flu.

8. Body cells that grow out of
   control and destroy other cells
   cause
   a. diabetes.
   (b.) cancer.
   c. antibodies.
   d. allergies.

9. A cure for the disease arthritis
   is
   a. eating fewer sweets and fatty
      foods.
   b. vaccines.
   c. antibiotics.
   (d.) not known yet.

10. Good health habits help
    prevent
    a. only communicable diseases.
    b. only heart diseases.
    c. allergies.
    (d.) both communicable and
       noncommunicable diseases.

Short Answer Write a C before each communicable
disease and an N before each noncommunicable disease.

_C_ 11. disease caused by a virus

_C_ 12. disease that can be prevented by a vaccine

_N_ 13. cardiovascular disease

_N_ 14. allergies

_N_ 15. diabetes

Short Essay Write your answers in complete sentences.

16. Why do antibiotics help the body fight some diseases
but not flu?

Antibiotics kill bacteria but not viruses. Flu

is caused by a virus.

17. How does the AIDS virus damage the body?

The AIDS virus can kill certain white blood cells that

normally help fight off disease germs. A person

can get diseases he or she cannot fight off.

18. What eating habits are important to a healthy lifestyle?

Answers might include: Eating fewer salty

and fatty foods helps keep the cardiovascular

system healthy. Eating fewer sweet, sugary

foods helps protect the teeth.

Name _____

Multiple Choice   Choose the best answer.

1. Everything that surrounds a person and affects him or her is
   a. a job.
   b. the environment.
   c. the community.
   d. a home.

2. To pollute means to
   a. make something dirty.
   b. make something smoky.
   c. drink dirty water.
   d. burn trash.

3. Tiny bits of solid material that float in the air and cause pollution are called
   a. gases.
   b. sewage.
   c. particles.
   d. fog.

4. Leaves and trash can be collected and burned without causing much pollution in
   a. an incinerator.
   b. a waste-treatment plant.
   c. a water-treatment plant.
   d. garbage cans.

5. Water is made safe to drink at a
   a. food factory.
   b. restaurant.
   c. waste-treatment plant.
   d. water-treatment plant.

6. What does a waste-treatment plant do?
   a. removes chemicals from water
   b. stores wastes in water
   c. treats sewage
   d. makes water safe to drink

7. One way to reduce noise pollution is to
   a. obey laws against honking horns too often.
   b. allow more jet planes to land.
   c. remove house rugs or drapes.
   d. cut down trees that surround houses.

8. Someone who checks food in restaurants and food factories is called
   a. a technician.
   b. a community inspector.
   c. a sanitarian.
   d. a food supplier.

9. Germs are killed when milk is
   a. cooled.
   b. pasteurized.
   c. stored in a dairy.
   d. inspected.

10. A community park helps many people
    a. find jobs.
    b. solve problems.
    c. hold meetings.
    d. have fun and feel good.

Short Answer   Read each cause of pollution. Tell whether it causes air pollution (A), water pollution (W), or noise pollution (N). Write the correct answer on the blank.

____ 11. smoke and gases from factories

____ 12. burning trash

____ 13. sewage

____ 14. chemicals from factories

____ 15. honking horns during a traffic jam

____ 16. jet planes flying very low over a city

Short Essay   Write your answers in complete sentences.

17. How could someone at a town meeting convince people that a scrubber is needed at a local factory?

_____

_____

_____

_____

18. What is wrong with mowing the lawn at seven o'clock in the morning?

_____

_____

_____

Multiple Choice   Choose the best answer.

1. What is a person's environment?
   a. the home that the person lives in
   b. the community that the person lives in
   c. the air that the person breathes
   d. everything that surrounds the person

2. When a factory makes the air and water dirty, it is
   a. helping the environment.
   b. wasting energy.
   c. using a scrubber.
   d. polluting.

3. Which of the following causes most air pollution?
   a. sewage
   b. burning
   c. airplanes
   d. yellow haze

4. One way a factory can help reduce air pollution is to
   a. install a furnace.
   b. install a scrubber.
   c. replace its smokestacks.
   d. install a waste-treatment plant.

5. Water that has wastes can be made safer if it is
   a. screened.
   b. heated.
   c. cooled.
   d. treated.

6. When water carrying wastes has been treated,
   a. it can no longer be returned to the water supply.
   b. it must be stored in a waste-treatment plant.
   c. it will be safe to drink.
   d. it can safely be returned to the water supply.

7. What can people do to protect the environment against pollution?
   a. obey the laws against littering
   b. burn leaves in the fall
   c. honk their horns at smoky cars
   d. drink bottled water

8. The job of a sanitarian is to
   a. check for water pollution.
   b. inspect food.
   c. look for air pollution.
   d. clean public places.

9. A food factory found to be handling food unsafely
   a. will have the restrooms checked.
   b. will be visited by nurses.
   c. might be closed.
   d. causes pollution.

10. Why do communities provide parks and playgrounds?
    a. for people to enjoy
    b. to make money.
    c. to reduce noise pollution.
    d. to reduce air pollution.

Short Answer   Match each meaning in Column I with the correct word in Column II. Write the correct letter on the blank.

Column I

_____ 11. tiny bits of material in the air

_____ 12. a furnace for burning trash

_____ 13. where wastes are made safe to dump into water

_____ 14. waste carried in sewers

_____ 15. where water is made safe to drink

_____ 16. to kill germs in milk

Column II

a. water-treatment plant

b. waste-treatment plant

c. sewage

d. incinerator

e. particles

f. pasteurize

Short Essay   Write your answers in complete sentences.

17. What laws might a city pass to reduce noise pollution?

_____

_____

_____.

18. A community sanitarian has found that a local dairy is unsafe. What might he or she do?

_____

_____

_____.

Multiple Choice   Choose the best answer.

1. Everything that surrounds
   a person and affects him or
   her is
   a. a job.
   b. the environment.
   c. the community.
   d. a home.

2. To pollute means to
   a. make something dirty.
   b. make something smoky.
   c. drink dirty water.
   d. burn trash.

3. Tiny bits of solid material that
   float in the air and cause
   pollution are called
   a. gases.
   b. sewage.
   c. particles.
   d. fog.

4. Leaves and trash can be
   collected and burned without
   causing much pollution in
   a. an incinerator.
   b. a waste-treatment plant.
   c. a water-treatment plant.
   d. garbage cans.

5. Water is made safe to drink
   at a
   a. food factory.
   b. restaurant.
   c. waste-treatment plant.
   d. water-treatment plant.

6. What does a waste-treatment
   plant do?
   a. removes chemicals from
      water
   b. stores wastes in water
   c. treats sewage
   d. makes water safe to drink

7. One way to reduce noise
   pollution is to
   a. obey laws against honking
      horns too often.
   b. allow more jet planes to land.
   c. remove house rugs or
      drapes.
   d. cut down trees that surround
      houses.

8. Someone who checks food in
   restaurants and food factories is
   called
   a. a technician.
   b. a community inspector.
   c. a sanitarian.
   d. a food supplier.

9. Germs are killed when milk is
   a. cooled.
   b. pasteurized.
   c. stored in a dairy.
   d. inspected.

10. A community park helps many
    people
    a. find jobs.
    b. solve problems.
    c. hold meetings.
    d. have fun and feel good.

Name _____

Short Answer   Read each cause of pollution. Tell
whether it causes air pollution (A), water pollution (W), or
noise pollution (N). Write the correct answer on the blank.

A 11. smoke and gases from factories

A 12. burning trash

W 13. sewage

W 14. chemicals from factories

N 15. honking horns during a traffic jam

N 16. jet planes flying very low over a city

Short Essay   Write your answers in complete sentences.

17. How could someone at a town meeting convince
people that a scrubber is needed at a local factory?

A person could explain that a scrubber will help

reduce the smoke, dust, and harmful gases put into

the air by the factory. This will make the air

in the community safer to breathe.

18. What is wrong with mowing the lawn at seven o'clock
in the morning?

The lawnmower will create noise pollution

that will disturb some people early

in the morning.

Multiple Choice   Choose the best answer.

1. What is a person's environment?
   a. the home that the person lives in
   b. the community that the person lives in
   c. the air that the person breathes
   (d.) everything that surrounds the person

2. When a factory makes the air and water dirty, it is
   a. helping the environment.
   b. wasting energy.
   c. using a scrubber.
   (d.) polluting.

3. Which of the following causes most air pollution?
   a. sewage
   (b.) burning
   c. airplanes
   d. yellow haze

4. One way a factory can help reduce air pollution is to
   a. install a furnace.
   (b.) install a scrubber.
   c. replace its smokestacks.
   d. install a waste-treatment plant.

5. Water that has wastes can be made safer if it is
   a. screened.
   b. heated.
   c. cooled.
   (d.) treated.

6. When water carrying wastes has been treated,
   a. it can no longer be returned to the water supply.
   b. it must be stored in a waste-treatment plant.
   c. it will be safe to drink.
   (d.) it can safely be returned to the water supply.

7. What can people do to protect the environment against pollution?
   (a.) obey the laws against littering
   b. burn leaves in the fall
   c. honk their horns at smoky cars
   d. drink bottled water

8. The job of a sanitarian is to
   a. check for water pollution.
   (b.) inspect food.
   c. look for air pollution.
   d. clean public places.

9. A food factory found to be handling food unsafely
   a. will have the restrooms checked.
   b. will be visited by nurses.
   (c.) might be closed.
   d. causes pollution.

10. Why do communities provide parks and playgrounds?
    (a.) for people to enjoy
    b. to make money.
    c. to reduce noise pollution.
    d. to reduce air pollution.

Short Answer Match each meaning in Column I with the correct word in Column II. Write the correct letter on the blank.

Column I

  e 11. tiny bits of material in the air

  d 12. a furnace for burning trash

  b 13. where wastes are made safe to dump into water

  c 14. waste carried in sewers

  a 15. where water is made safe to drink

  f 16. to kill germs in milk

Column II

a. water-treatment plant

b. waste-treatment plant

c. sewage

d. incinerator

e. particles

f. pasteurize

Short Essay Write your answers in complete sentences.

17. What laws might a city pass to reduce noise pollution?

Answers might include: laws requiring soundproof

materials in buildings, reducing air traffic

near houses, quieter trucks and motorcycles.

18. A community sanitarian has found that a local dairy is unsafe. What might he or she do?

The sanitarian might discuss with dairy operators ways

to solve the problem; follow up to see that corrections

have been made; and if not, close the dairy down.